HOW TO STUDY MATH

Helen Burrier
Kirkwood Community College

A Division of Simon & Schuster
Englewood Cliffs, N.J. 07632

25 24 23

ISBN: 0-13-020884-1

Printed in the United States of America

TABLE OF CONTENTS

INTRODUCTION

As you begin a new course in mathematics, you may find it quite helpful to read carefully the suggestions and helpful hints given in this booklet. Here I have outlined for you the proper approach to the study of mathematics. There is no magic formula that will place you on the path towards success in mathematics; but these suggestions, when followed carefully, will lead you in the right direction. You will find that regular study and daily practice are necessary efforts to strengthen your skills and to help you grow academically.

Perhaps you are thinking, "But I have never been any good at mathematics," or "I have always hated mathematics," or "Math always scares me," or " I have not had any math for so long that I have forgotten it all". You may have picked up on the label "Math Anxiety" and attached it to yourself. That is most unfortunate, and I would suggest that you reprogram your thinking. Replace those negative thoughts with more positive ones. You may say things like, "I will give this math class my best shot," or "I can learn mathematics if I work at it", or "I will try to do better than I have done in previous math classes". You will be pleasantly surprised at the difference this makes!

In the technological world we live in, giving up on math can prevent you from pursuing a number of careers that could be valid choices if only a few math courses were taken. That doesn't necessarily mean that you need to go as far as calculus, but it might include taking such courses as intermediate algebra, finite math, college algebra, or trigonometry. You see, learning mathematics can open new doors for you.

Learning mathematics is a process that takes time and effort. The suggestions and helpful hints given in this booklet will aid you in the process, as they will lead you towards success in mathematics. As you become more successful, your confidence in your ability to do mathematics will grow.

Remember: You can take charge and be responsible for your own learning. You will mature as a student and will benefit immensely from it.

CLASS ATTENDANCE

In order to be successful in mathematics, you must choose to attend class on a regular basis, beginning with the first day of class! Statistics have definitely shown that grades improve with better attendance. Every time you miss a class, you miss some vital information that can hamper your understanding of even basic concepts. Someone else's notes are a poor substitute for the direct learning possible in the classroom. Get off to a good start by setting a goal to attend class every day.

CLASS PARTICIPATION

Be willing to be involved in the class as an active participant. Sit towards the front, ask questions, contribute toward solutions, and be interested in the class activities. In order to be successful, you must be involved as a participant, not on the sidelines as a spectator. Your contributions are valuable and worthwhile to the class and to yourself. The more involved you are, the more you will learn. Do yourself a favor and try it!

PREVIEWING NEW MATERIAL

Before going to class each day, take a few minutes to look over the sections in your text that are scheduled to be covered that day. You do not necessarily need to study and learn the material on your own, but a survey of the concepts, terminology, diagrams, and examples will help the new ideas seem more familiar as the instructor presents them. You will be able to see what is coming, which may help you be prepared with possible questions.

READING THE TEXTBOOK

You need to read carefully every day the sections assigned in your textbook. Your instructor has chosen this text to aid in your learning, so take advantage and allow it to work for you. I think you will find that you will get your money's worth!

Reading a mathematics textbook is unlike reading many other types of books that you may find in your literature, history, psychology, or sociology courses. Reading a mathematics text takes more effort and more time. One page could even take thirty minutes or more, because a mathematics text is a technical book that needs slow and careful reading.

Begin reading your textbook with a paper and pencil in hand. When you read a new definition, property, or theorem, underline it in the text and/or write it down. Whenever you encounter an unfamiliar term, look it up and make a note of it. When you come to an example, work through it with the author. Be sure to read each word and to follow directions carefully.

You cannot hurry this procedure. Take your time, invest some of yourself, and make sure you are understanding what you are reading. The only skimming of a mathematics text that can occur is perhaps during the review time before an exam.

TAKING NOTES IN CLASS

In order to take meaningful notes, you must be an active listener. Keep your mind on what the instructor is saying, and be ready to ask questions whenever you do not understand something.

Write down important ideas and examples as the instructor lectures, making sure that you are listening and following the logic. If you have previewed the lesson material, you will be prepared to take more meaningful notes. The important concepts will make sense, and you will realize what needs to be written down. If you frantically try to write down all the instructor says, or mindlessly copy down all examples done in class, you may find your notes to be nearly worthless when you are home alone. To think that you will write it down now and attempt to understand it later is a serious mistake. Listen, process, and ask questions during appropriate times. Be involved in the class, mentally and verbally.

MAKING A FRIEND IN THE CLASS

Attempt to make a friend in your class. You may find you enjoy sitting together and drawing support and encouragement from one another. Study together whenever possible. You must not depend on a friend or fellow student to tutor you, do your work for you, or in any way be responsible for your learning. However, it is possible for you to learn from one another as you seek to master the given concepts. You may be more successful and find it to be more fun if you study with someone else, comparing notes, methods, and answers.

GETTING HELP

Getting the right kind of help at the right time can be a key ingredient to being successful in algebra. When you have gone to class on a regular basis, taken careful notes, methodically read your textbook, diligently done your homework, thus making every effort possible to learn the mathematical skills, you may find that you are still having difficulty. If this is the case, then you need to seek help. Make an appointment with your instructor to find out what help is available to you in the form of instructor time, tutoring service, a mathematics lab, video tapes, or computer software.

Once you discover the resources available in your school, you need to take advantage of them. Do not put it off, or you will find yourself getting behind. You cannot afford that!

Remember: When studying mathematics, you must keep up with your work.

HOMEWORK ASSIGNMENTS

Keep in mind that mathematics is a skill that can only be learned and mastered by doing it yourself with lots and lots of practice. There is no other way. Think of it as being similar to learning to play a musical instrument, learning to type, or playing a sport. No matter how much you watch someone else do it, how many books you may read on "how to" do it, or how easy it may seem to be, the key to success is practice.

Set aside some time <u>each</u> <u>day</u> for your homework assignments. Do not attempt to do a whole week's worth on the weekend. That is disaster! A minimum of two hours spent studying outside of class for each hour in class is usually required for college courses. You may need much more for mathematics.

Work on your assignments every day and do as many problems as it takes for you to know what you are doing, to become really skilled in each concept. Sometimes this may mean that you do many more problems than the instructor assigns. Never do less than what has been assigned. You must assume responsibility for your own learning; therefore <u>you</u> have to decide how much is enough.

Before you start your homework problems, read your textbook very carefully. Expect to spend much more time reading a few pages of a mathematics textbook than several pages of another text.

As you begin your homework assignments, read the directions carefully. You need to understand what is being asked for. Concentrate on each problem, taking time to solve accurately. Rushing through your work usually causes costly errors. Check your answers with those given in the back of the textbook. If your answer is incorrect, check to see if you are doing the right problem or if you have copied it down correctly. Redo the problem, watching for little errors. If it is still wrong, check with a friend. Perhaps the two of you can figure it out. If you still cannot figure it out, ask your instructor for help. You may even find that an error has occurred in the textbook.

For those problems you seem unable to do, check the examples in the text or in your notes for a similar type. See if this one can be solved in the same way. Give the problem some thought. You may want to leave it for awhile, taking a break or doing a different one. But come back later and try again. If you still cannot figure it out on your own or with the help of a friend, ask your instructor for help.

SOLVING APPLICATIONS OR WORD PROBLEMS

Applications or word problems are the very life of mathematics! They teach you how to use the mathematical skills you have developed. Learning mathematics without doing word problems is similar to learning all the skills of a sport without ever playing a game or learning all the notes and scales on an instrument without ever playing a song.

The first step in your approach to word problems is to reprogram your thinking. Delete your previous thoughts such as, "I never have been able to do word problems" or "I can't figure out what to do in word problems". Replace those negative thoughts with the following: "I can do some word problems. With a little effort and practice, I will be able to do more than I could before".

Again, the key to success is practice. Make yourself do as many problems as you can. You may not be able to do them all correctly, but keep trying. Do not give up whenever you reach a difficult one. If you cannot solve it, just try another one. Then come back and try it again later.

A misconception among students when they begin studying algebra is that each problem is different. At first they may seem this way, but as you practice more and more, you will begin to see the similarities, the different "types". This will aid in your solutions.

Most textbooks give you a list of steps to guide you in your approach to word problems. They will, more or less, include the following:

1. Read the problem carefully, as many times as necessary to understand what the problem is saying and asking for.

   Unfortunately some students misunderstand or ignore this step. Instead of reading for understanding, they read the problem with the thought, "How am I going to solve this problem?", repeating itself in their minds. Watch out for this, as it will block your reasoning process.

2. Make diagrams, charts, or drawings to help you visualize the problem.

   This is a very important step that allows you to see the relationship between the various parts of the problem.

3. Identify the variable to be used for the unknown quantity.

   Be specific. Label clearly what "x" will be in your solution. Be sure to include the units of measure, if applicable. Students are often careless with this step, and it usually leads to confusion. At the end of their solution, they are not sure just what they have found.

4. Look for a formula or relationship that exists in the problem. Write the equation that shows this relationship using the variable you have identified in Step 3.

   Students sometimes want to jump into this step too quickly. Remember, it is Step 4. Look to see that the equation makes sense, that it shows the relationship accurately.

5. Solve the equation.

   Watch out for decimal points and negative signs - the little errors that cause BIG problems.

6. Read the problem again to see if you have found what the problem asks for. Perhaps more than one answer is needed.

7. Check your answer.

   Does it work? Does it make sense? Watch for negative answers and fractional answers. Can they exist?

Remember: The only way to be successful with word problems is to practice solving as many as possible. KEEP TRYING AND DON'T GIVE UP!

STUDYING FOR AN EXAM

When the time comes for you to take an exam, there are some things that you must realize in order to prepare adequately.

1. You are on your own. You cannot get help from anyone, and you will probably not be allowed to use notes or textbooks.

2. Your time will be limited.

3. Many different kinds of problems will be included from one or more chapters.

4. You may experience a high level of anxiety, thus preventing clear thinking and causing careless errors.

In order to prepare adequately for an exam, you must begin early. Spread your review time out over a period of days, studying one to two hours at a time. This will take the pressure off, giving you time to relax and rest your brain a little. You will also have what is called process time, the time to reflect and tie together what you have been learning.

To review for the exam, you will need to:

1. Reread your notes and textbook.

2. Study new terminology, definitions, and properties, often set off in boxes in your textbook. Be sure you understand their meaning.

3. Practice some of each type of problem covered in the chapter(s) you are to be tested over. Watch out for common student errors.

4. Use the end of chapter materials provided in your textbook. If there is a glossary or chapter summary, carefully read through them. Do the review exercises. If there is a practice test, take it as though it were the exam itself. When you are finished, check your answers. Redo any problems you missed, and look up any you were unable to solve.

5. Get help for those concepts where you are having difficulty.

DO NOT stay up late studying the night before the exam. Get a good nights rest, and allow yourself plenty of time to get to your exam. This will help you to feel better prepared and, therefore, more relaxed. If you feel less anxious, your brain will function better and your thoughts will be clearer.

TAKING AN EXAM

After you get your exam, you will find it helpful to do the following:

1. Take a few seconds for two or three moderately deep breaths. Inhale, then exhale slowly. You will feel your body relax.

2. Write down on the back of the exam any formulas or ideas that you must remember.

3. Look over the entire test quickly in order to pace yourself and be able to use your time wisely. Make note of the point count given for each problem. Spend more time on items of greater worth.

4. Read directions carefully, and be sure to answer all questions completely. Indicate final answers clearly. Keep your work neat.

5. Work the problems and answer the questions that are easiest for you first. Then come back to the more difficult ones.

6. Do not get bogged down on one problem too long, as it may jeopardize your chances of being able to finish several problems in the time you are spending on one.

7. Check your work in the time remaining. This will help you catch minor errors.

8. Stay calm if others leave before you do. You are entitled to use the full amount of time allotted.

Remember: There is no quick and easy way to learn mathematics. You will need to work hard with diligent, systematic practice. Following these guidelines, however, will help make studying mathematics easier and more enjoyable with quite satisfying results.

APPLYING MATHEMATICS TO YOUR WORLD

Students often question the value of mathematics, particularly algebra, and ask when and where they can use it. In the technological world that we live in, one has only to look around and see the unlimited uses of mathematics. We use it to build, construct, travel, discover, buy, invest, compare, evaluate, plan, and get ahead, to name a few. The specialized areas of trigonometry, calculus, and statistics are so widely applicable that most college majors require their students to take one or more of these classes. However, before these classes can be taken, the basic algebra skills must be mastered.

As you study and learn mathematics, you will become aware of more and more uses for it. As you become more skillful, taking more courses, your opportunities and choices will increase and doors will open. Then you will not have to ask the question, "When or where will I ever use this stuff?" You will know the answer.

PRENTICE HALL, ENGLEWOOD CLIFFS, NEW JERSEY 07632

0-13-020884-1